Q5O TUR

First Edition, August 2001
Author: Alison Turnbull
Copyright the Foundation of Nursing Studies 2001
ISBN: 0-9540091-0-X
Illustrator: Andy Tristram
Publishers: The Foundation of Nursing Studies
Printers: Jaggerprint – 020 8546 0593

The Plain Words Team

Plain Words for Nurses: Writing and Communicating Effectively has been a team effort. First, Elizabeth Stallwood and Fay Buglass of the Foundation of Nursing Studies believed me when I told them there was a clearer way for nurses to write. They agreed to host a FoNS workshop on plain words in the summer of 1998.

The book has grown from there. Along the way, a team of people have diligently emailed, faxed and posted helpful and inspirational comments and examples of not-so-plain words. They are:

Jo Armes,   Research Nurse, St Christopher's Hospice, Sydenham, London

Denis Anthony,   Professor of Nursing Informatics, Mary Seacole Research Centre, School of Nursing and Midwifery, De Montfort University, Leicester

Peter Birchenall,   Lincoln Co-operative Society Professor of Health Studies, University of Lincolnshire and Humberside

Simon Breed,   Course Director, Writing Workshops for Nurses

Fay Buglass,   Director, Foundation of Nursing Studies

Pamela de Clive-Lowe,   Research Sister, Department of Clinical Biochemistry, Addenbrooke's NHS Trust, Cambridge

Terry Denman,   Trainer, Plain English Campaign

Tom Dodd,   Lead in Assertive Outreach, The Foundation NHS Trust, Stafford

Gillian Fletcher,   Trainer, National Childbirth Trust/College of Health

Carole Hopps,   Lecturer-Practitioner, School of Nursing and Midwifery, Sheffield University

Gill Husband,   Senior Lecturer, Nursing Practice & Research, City Hospitals Sunderland NHS Trust and University of Sunderland

Mei-Lin Law,   Lecturer Practitioner, Faculty of Health and Social Care, University of the West of England, Bristol

Anne Lowis,   Professor of Nursing, Robert Gordon University, Aberdeen

Paul Mangan,   Webmaster, *internurse.com*

Christina Martin,   Public Relations Officer, Down Lisburn Health and Social Services Trust, Co Antrim

Ann McDonnell, MRC Training Fellow, Medical Care Research Unit, School of Health and Related Research (ScHARR), University of Sheffield

Clare McNamara, Sister, Paediatric Unit, Royal Preston Acute NHS Hospital Trust

Matthew Pulzer, Editor, RCM Midwives' Journal, Royal College of Midwives

Leah Roberts, Doctoral Student, Essex University

Jim Robinson, Lecturer in Children's Nursing, Royal Hospital for Sick Children, Lothian University Hospitals NHS Trust; and Department of Nursing Studies, University of Edinburgh

Helen Scott, Editor, British Journal of Nursing

Theresa Shaw, Professional Development Officer, Foundation of Nursing Studies

Jackie Solomon, Senior Nurse Research and Development, Bolton Hospitals NHS Trust

Elizabeth Stallwood, Vice-Chair, Foundation of Nursing Studies

Phil Walmsley, Senior Nurse Manager, Children's Services, Nottingham City Hospital

Rod Ward, Lecturer in Nursing and Health Informatics, Department of Acute and Critical Care, University of Sheffield

Christine Webb, Professor of Health Studies, University of Plymouth; and Editor, Journal of Clinical Nursing

Liz Welch, Communications & IT Co-ordinator, Foundation of Nursing Studies

And finally, 3M Health Care for their sponsorship to publish this book.

Acknowledgements
For the example of a long sentence in Chapter 2: Nursing Standard

For the examples of Plain English in patient literature, used as exercises in Chapter 12:
Southern Birmingham Community Health NHS Trust
Hairmyres and Stonehouse Hospitals NHS Trust
Glasgow Royal Infirmary NHS Trust
York District Hospital

For the definition of a bed in Chapter 12: Plain English Campaign

Alison Turnbull, July 2001

Contents

Introduction

Why Plain Words?

Between 1994 and 1996, the Foundation of Nursing Studies (FoNS) held four conferences to explore how nursing research is disseminated and implemented. This was one of the barriers the delegates identified:

'Research reports are jargonistic, inaccessible, and their implications for practice are unclear...Researchers are intimidating' (FoNS 1997).

This means that researchers are working their socks off to gather and disseminate the best evidence – and scrabbling around for funds to continue their work – but the evidence is not going where it is needed. Teachers are unsure what to include in their curricula, while busy practitioners may not have enough time to plough through all the research and identify best practice. Nurses may also find it hard to explain their practice to patients.

In many journal articles the implications for practice are hard to find because they are wrapped up in long words and phrases. You can read them – but you cannot always make sense of them and turn them into your own good practice.

You may also be afraid to submit your own work for publication because you believe that there is only one 'correct' way to write.

I want to make sure that you can read and clearly understand the nursing literature and so make the best use of it in practice.

Alison Turnbull

Chapter 1

Clear writing

1: Clear writing

Clear writing is like caring for roses. Cut off the dead heads and prune the puny shoots and you will have beautiful blooms. People will see and remember the blooms. Let your garden become a jungle and people will only see and remember the jungle.

Imagine the blooms as your implications for practice. They are golden nuggets of evidence that you have spent a long time investigating, that you want someone else to go away and use – today.

In 'Plain Words for Nurses' I don't want you to think about the blooms but to think about the jungle – the dead heads and the puny shoots – and ask yourself:

- are they really necessary, or do they obscure my good work?

- do busy nurses have time to hack through them?

More room in journals
In many journal articles the implications for practice are hard to find because they are wrapped up in long-winded words and phrases. You can read these articles – you are educated and literate – but don't you sometimes feel that you are wading through treacle? Have you got the author's message, or have you misread it entirely?

If people could write more clearly and more concisely, there would be more room in journals for their work to be published. Journals could cover more topics, and offer more variety. Instead of two six-page monsters you could read four snappy three-pagers and two more authors would be published.

There would be more room for tables and illustrations, and even room for the white space that graphic designers and editors often disagree about. Editors try to cram in as many words as they can, but designers want their creations to 'breathe'. Reading tight-packed small print is hard. Words are much easier to read if they are in larger type with more space between the lines and between the columns.

Readability

Gunning and Kallan (1994) called the superfluous words and phrases 'Fog'. They define Fog as 'unnecessary complexity [that] arises from frozen phrases and windy expressions. Fogged prose never sounds natural.'

Gunning devised a measure of readability called the Fog Index. You may have come across this already, along with other measures of readability and 'grade level'. But I don't think that 'readability' is something that you can put into figures. In the time it takes you to calculate a readability score there are more practical steps you can take to make your work more readable.

Confident style

Nurses need masses of new knowledge to keep up with their work. But they don't need that knowledge wrapped up in unnecessary baggage. I want to make sure that readers of your work get your message quickly and make the best use of it in their practice. This usually means shorter, tighter writing, but not always. Sometimes you will need more words to spell out your message.

You can develop a confident, fluent and personal style of writing without losing your academic credibility. 'Plain Words for Nurses' shows you how.

The benefits of clear writing

**Clear writing is a step towards better practice.
If you can write clearly you can:**
- avoid wasteful duplication of work
- be published in a wider range of journals
- change your practice
- communicate with other health professionals
- communicate with patients
- improve people's perception of what nurses do and know
- justify your decisions
- keep better records
- make research and case studies more understandable
- promote further discussion about your subject
- raise the profile of nurses and nursing
- save time – yours and other people's
- see the patient's point of view
- share your good practice with more people

Chapter 2

Shorten your sentences

2: Shorten your sentences

Whatever their educational level, readers get lost in long sentences. Sometimes you may feel that the writer is also lost. Can you follow what is happening in the next paragraph?

'Based broadly on these principles though not on a rigorous application of their injunctions in detail, an endless and almost impossible set of requirements, my research study was designed to involve a progressive building up from the direct gathering of data across sites, events and methods in ways that allow themes to emerge and re-emerge before and after initially looking for and being willing to modify their theoretical and practical status.' (71 words, 1 sentence)

This sentence was edited and appeared in 'Nursing Standard' as:
'This study was broadly, but not rigorously, based on these principles. The aim was to build up progressively from directly gathering data across sites, events and methods in ways that allowed themes to emerge and re-emerge.' (11 + 24 words in 2 sentences)

Use your word processor
Some people swear by their word processing software – others swear at it. Mine is a trusted friend. I can do things on screen that I cannot do on paper.

Think big
Whatever the state of your eyesight, think big. Surgeons use powerful magnifying equipment – why shouldn't you? When you are working on screen there is no need to squint unless your computer is very old and only offers one size of text. My software lets me view text at different magnifications. I set my font to 12 point Arial and blow up the text to 125% (one and a quarter times actual size). My paragraphs are much easier to read, I can sit back from the computer and I don't get all hunched up and stiff when I am working.

Read out loud
Read through your work, out loud. When you breathe, that's where the full stop should go. Read it to someone else. If they look puzzled or lost you may need to rewrite the sentence.

Write one sentence for one idea
Use your word processor to search for commas and colons. Would a full stop look better? Take care when you use:

- and
- or
- but
- not only…but also

These little words often link unconnected ideas.

Make lists
You can break up sentences with long lists, separated by commas, into bullet pointed lists with a new idea on every line. Many printed journals accept articles with bullet points, and lists make web pages much easier to read on screen. There, bullet point items can be programmed as 'hot spots' – readers click their mouse on the item to navigate faster to topics that interest them.

You can also use a bullet list as a checklist to make sure that you cover all the points you intend. It is surprising how many people introduce their work by saying: 'This article will cover:

- subject a
- theme c
- topic b
- idea d'

…and then forget to include idea 'd' altogether.

You can make the list into a box or table. This can help the journal's designer to make your article look more interesting, but beware – too many bullet lists can be hard to read without text to link them.

Count your words
Gunning and Kallan (1994) recommend an average sentence length of 15-20 words. Vary the length of your sentences – a series of short bursts can irritate the reader as much as long sentences.

You may be able to set the grammar checker on your word processor to weed out sentences longer than 20 words. When these sentences are highlighted on screen, think how you might shorten them.

An easier way, if you work with 12 point text blown up to 125%, is to watch out for sentences longer than two lines.

Chapter 3

Answer the question

3: Answer the question

The first thing a junior reporter learns on a newspaper is that the news editor wants **answers**. Answers to questions such as:

- who?
- where?
- how much?
- when?
- how long?
- how many?

Nurses, so expert at record keeping and accountability, often disguise these skills with woolly writing that leaves questions unanswered. How much is 'a certain amount'? How far is 'to a greater or lesser degree'? When is the 'not too distant future'? If something is 'difficult, if not impossible' just how hard is it?

Who?
'It has been suggested that...'

- who suggested it?
- where are your references?
- when?

'It was decided...'

- who decided?
- why?
- when?
- was there opposition?

When?
You do not always have to cut back your words to make your meaning clear.

You could prune 'in the not-too-distant future' or 'as soon as possible' to 'soon'. But if there has been a time lag between submitting an article to a journal and having it published, 'soon' and 'the end of the year' may be meaningless or ambiguous.

It is better, if you can, to set yourself a time, date or deadline, for example:

'We hope the results of this audit will be ready in the not too distant future.'
becomes
'We hope to publish the results of this audit by the end of April 2002.'

The second sentence is not much shorter, but it is more positive and tells your reader much more about the energy you are putting into your project (even if your deadline is stretched into mid-June.)

What do you mean by 'short term' or ' recent past'? Are you counting in days, months or years? It is more helpful if you say exactly what you mean.

'At this moment in time' and 'with immediate effect' are just woolly ways of saying 'now'. If you are clear that something is happening now, or about to happen, now will do.

'Expected imminently' and 'within an immediate time frame' are woolly ways of saying 'soon', and 'a period of twelve months' is always 'a year'.

Where?
You know where you are, and what population your trust or college serves. Your reader may not. They will interpret these words in different ways:

- vicinity
- district
- locale
- region
- neighbourhood
- catchment area
- local population

They will be more confused if they are in another country where neighbourhoods and catchment areas cover more square miles but fewer people. If you can, try to define the area you are talking about in terms of either population or square kilometres – or both.

How long?
'The catheter must be kept in place for a further period of time.'

- how long – an hour, 12, 24, 48 hours, a week?
- who will decide when it can be taken out?
- how will they decide?

How much?
'Additional funds may be required'

- how much money – hundreds, thousands, tens of thousands?
- who are you approaching for money?
- how are you going to raise the funds?
- when do you think the funds will be available?

Although they are vague, words such as:

- some
- many
- few
- most

help your writing to flow when you do not need to give exact figures. Other woolly phrases don't tell your reader anything, for example:

- little or no
- not a great deal
- to a greater or lesser degree
- to varying degrees
- by and large
- in some measure
- a certain amount
- more or less
- to a certain extent

How many?
'Study days were poorly attended'

- how many people came?
- how many people were asked and didn't come?
- why do you think there was such a poor turnout?
- what are you doing about it?

What is a 'vast' or an 'overwhelming' majority? What is a 'substantial' number?' Are they more than 50%, 75% or 90%? 'Vast' suggests that you have an enormous sample size,' overwhelming' that you are knee deep in paperwork. Instead, try:

- more than 75%
- more than three quarters; or, simply
- most.

Be a good reporter – try not to leave any questions hanging unanswered.

Exercise
How would you improve these phrases?

1. Almost always
2. Due in no small measure to
3. A period of 14 days
4. A vast majority

(suggestions on page 79)

Chapter 4

Be active

WHAT A PERFORMANCE!

4: Be active

Nurses are positive and active, but this is not always clear in their writing. Would this sentence inspire you to go and find out more about the theories of change?

'An understanding of the theories of change and how to facilitate change strategies could improve nurses' effectiveness.'

Try: 'Nurses can work more effectively if they understand how the theories of change apply to their practice.'

This puts you, the nurse, firmly in the driving seat, able to decide for yourself what you need to do and read to work more effectively.

Who is 'doing' in this woolly sentence?

'Appreciation has been shown in the form of written letters from patients thanking us for our care.'

Answer: the patients. They have been moved to put pen to paper and thank you for something you have done. If you loudly applaud their efforts, you will applaud your own.

Try: 'Patients have written appreciative letters to thank us for our care.'

For every sentence that involves a person – a nurse or a patient, a reader or a writer – try to put that person – the subject – first. Make them do, not be done to. As you read through the examples opposite, cover the right-hand column with a sheet of paper. See if you can work out who is doing the action, and make them the subject of the sentence.

Passive (something is or was done)	Active (somebody does or did something)
Concern was expressed by staff	Staff were worried about...
The goal of the nurse should be	Nurses should aim to
Views were sought from patients	The researcher asked patients to comment
A fee may be payable	The patient may have to pay
In order for an informed choice to be made by the patient	To give the patient enough information to make a choice
Fear may be experienced by patients	Patients may be frightened or
	Patients may fear...
A pronounced improvement was observed in the patient's condition	Be specific – for example:
	The patient felt better
	The patient's blood pressure went down to...
	The patient felt less pain
	The patient had fewer episodes of...

Aren't we meant to write in the passive?

If you are doing the action you might like to use 'I' or 'We' – the first person singular or plural. But some journal editors prefer you not to use the first person. They argue that it is subjective and unprofessional and allows emotions to creep in. They prefer the third person – he, she, it and they. Do you think 'The author undertook a literature review' sounds more professional than 'I reviewed the literature...?' Does 'We noted...' have more emotion than 'The research team observed ...?'

If you plan to send an article to a particular journal:
- read back issues to get a feel for the style
- ask for a copy of the authors' guidelines
- if you are still not clear, talk to the editor about the style he or she prefers

Hamill (1999) suggests some occasions when it might be appropriate to write in the first person:
- case studies
- reflective diaries/journals
- critical incident analyses
- reporting qualitative research findings
- submitting accreditation of prior experiential learning/accreditation of prior learning (APEL/APL evidence)
- preparing post registration education and practice (PREP) submissions
- writing a personal opinion article for publication

Here are some other ways you can use the first person:

Third Person	First Person
A study was undertaken to assess the use of	We studied how people used
The patient was notified	We told the patient or
	We wrote to the patient
Advice was sought from .... regarding	We asked .... about ....

Inanimate objects
Buildings often appear to do things that bricks and mortar cannot do, for example: 'The hospital is planning...' 'The clinic wrote to...'

Only people – for example, the clinical team, the trust manager, the practice nurse – can plan, take responsibility, make decisions and write letters.

Shun '-tion'

Often the suffixes 'tion' and 'sion' take the action out of verbs – and take up more space. Cover the right-hand column as you read down the list of examples below, and see if you can improve on them.

Phrase	Suggested alternative
a possible explanation for this may be	this may be because or this may be the result of
at the time of hospitalisation	on admission when the patient was admitted
cause disruption	disrupt
consideration should be given to	think about, consider...
give a description	describe
give an indication of	show
have an appreciation of	appreciate
make the best utilisation of resources	maximise, optimise
make a distinction	distinguish, show the difference
provide with an explanation	explain
streamline the documentation	edit
show a reduction	reduce

What a performance

Many writers use 'performed' where 'done' or the past tense would do, for example:

- a urine test was performed
- a caesarean section was performed
- site cleansing was performed

No doubt some theatre sisters would describe surgical operations as a dramatic performance, with the surgeon in the leading role. But while a surgeon might perform a caesarean to Wagner with a flourish of the scalpel there is little scope for high drama in urine tests or wound care. Try:

- urine was tested
- the site was cleaned

The passives are fine here because the active alternative can be long-winded.

Exercise

Who is the subject in these phrases? Rewrite the phrases with the subject first. Answers on page 79.

1. There has been reluctance on the part of GPs to...

2. These surveys are completed by patients

3. It is recommended that ...

4. Find an article you have written. Use your word processor to find words that end in -sion and -tion. Have you used any of these words where a verb will do? Think how you would re-write the sentences where you have used these words.

Chapter 5
Challenge jargon

5: Challenge jargon

What is jargon?

No word or phrase is jargon if everybody who uses it understands it in the same way. But if you pass on a word or phrase, you must:

- understand it yourself; and
- make sure that the next person – patient or professional – understands it in the same way

Otherwise you are talking jargon.

Keep your audience in mind

Your writing will not be effective if your readers feel left out because they do not understand some of the words. Jargon is not something you can list neatly – all words mean something to somebody. Jargon depends on the context and the audience, for whom you are writing. Gunning and Kallan (1994) say:

'Words don't have fixed meanings. For each person, the meaning of any word includes those personal experiences associated with it.'

Breed (1999) says:

'There is a difference between the use of acceptable jargon, which has concrete and unambiguous meaning for every member of the audience who reads it, and the type of convoluted terminology that so many authors throw into their articles because they think it sounds more impressive.'

'Sorry, what did you say?'

Chinese Whispers is a fun game for children – though it is probably not 'politically correct' to call it that now. Players sit in a circle. Player 1 whispers a phrase into Player 2's ear. Player 2 looks puzzled and passes on what he thinks he has heard to Player 3, and so it goes.

For example:
Systemic lupus erythematosus could become:

- Sister Mac's loopy arithmetic doses
- sit on the loo, please, Mr Moses
- Mister Smith has halitosis
- mushy mushy mushy

The last child usually collapses in giggles and makes nothing of the original at all.

Mangling the words in the game makes it more fun – we find a context and we try to make it fit so that the person next to us can also make something of it. But if we mangle words and phrases in our work we can pass on misunderstandings to other health professionals or – worse – to patients.

'I'm not familiar with that'

Often jargon slips through because people are afraid to challenge it. A journalist colleague of mine went to a press launch of a new fax machine. The managing director of the fax company proudly announced that the machine came complete with LRF. 'LRF?' said my friend bravely. 'I'm sorry, I'm not familiar with that term.' 'Little Rubber Feet!' laughed the director. 'And do you know, you're the first person brave enough to ask?'

How many of us have the courage in conferences and lectures to put up our hands and say 'excuse me, what do you mean by ...?' or 'I'm not familiar with that'? I suspect that many of us keep quiet for fear of looking stupid.

'Could you explain that, please?'

Tom Dodd, from Foundation NHS Trust, Stafford, says: 'The team that I work with presented some thoughts on risk assessment. We read out lists of words for guidance on what to look for or assess in a number of areas. It sounded very impressive, but when we asked who in the team actually understood what the words meant, we found that few of us did.'

'We decided it was easier to notice "how people in the family got on together" rather than "record the structure of dynamics between significant others" and to "make a note of what the neighbourhood is like" rather than "define any high risk geographical factors detrimental to lone working". This made sure that we all knew what information we were after. Everyone in the team (health care support workers, psychologist, nurses, occupational therapists, pharmacist) needs to be speaking and understanding the same language – especially when assessing risk.'

'We probably don't challenge jargon enough, but when we have it's usually come as a bit of a relief when someone has been brave enough to do so. I think one way to help prevent this is to nurture a culture that refuses to allow people to get away with it.'

'I attended a workshop some months ago with a friend who works in the voluntary sector. A well-known psychologist was presenting some work on "locality profiling", and was challenged to use plain English by my friend, after about fifteen minutes of jargon and "management-speak". The psychologist apologised, but just couldn't resist the temptation to camouflage his presentation in ambiguous and confusing language.'

Pamela de Clive-Lowe, Research Sister in the Department of Clinical Biochemistry at Addenbrooke's NHS Trust, Cambridge, says: 'There is often a fear of showing ourselves up, which I am sure stems back to most people's school days and the fear of being ridiculed. Yet sometimes if you question people who are trying to "blind you with science" they become unstuck. They do not really know themselves what they are talking about, and may even be embarrassed when they realise that an explanation is beyond them.'

'But I thought that meant…'
Authors often interpret and define terms in different ways. There may be two or more schools of thought on the subject you are covering. If so, you need to start with a short paragraph or box explaining whose definition you are using in your article or presentation – and why you consider that definition is more appropriate. This may be a subjective choice, but gives your reader or listener a starting point.

Be brave: challenge jargon whenever you can.

Exercise
Can you think of any idea – from childhood or adult life – that you have accepted, used, passed on and then realised later that you were wrong?

How would you explain that idea to another person about to make the same mistake?

Chapter 6

Say it only once

6: Say it only once

We use many phrases that say the same thing twice. You can only plan for the future, and you can only experience something that has already happened. ~~Forward~~ planning and ~~previous~~ experience each have a word you don't need.

Common repetitions

Example	Comment
subsequent result	results are always subsequent
clearly understand	if it's not clear, you won't understand it
consequent effect	effects are always consequent
in contrast, this is quite different	in contrast or this is different, but not both
my own personal experience	no-one can have your experience but you
ongoing audit cycle	a cycle is ongoing
previously validated	validated is already in the past tense
quite unique	something is either unique or it's not

Cross it out

continues ~~to this day~~	~~general~~ consensus
reiterate ~~again~~	improve ~~even further~~
includes ~~among other things~~	~~still~~ persist
this will continue ~~as an ongoing process~~	~~ultimately~~ responsible
while ~~at the same time~~	report ~~back~~

Two's a crowd

- each and every
- tried and tested
- trials and tribulations
- if and when
- over and above
- difficult, if not impossible

Add-ons
Some words can help you link one paragraph to the next. They include:

- additionally
- other
- further, furthermore
- added
- as well as
- also
- also

But you only need one at a time – 'additionally, there are also further…' uses three!

Too many alsos can devalue the next point you make. If you are moving on to a new theme introduce it confidently – perhaps with a heading of its own.

Exercise
Cross out the redundant words in these phrases. Answers on page 79
- developing further
- in circumstances where
- my own
- still ongoing
- then subsequently
- yet another
- consensus of opinion

Chapter 7

Keep it in perspective

7: Keep it in perspective

Sometimes in the flow of writing you want your reader to pay more attention. You will search for an extra word or phrase to add emphasis. This is good. But it is easy to become over-enthusiastic about your work, and soon all your paragraphs may contain one of the words or phrases below.

These words are like salt and pepper – you need to add a little seasoning to keep the reader interested in what you have to say. Add too much and your reader will not be able to digest your work. If the word 'important' appears in every paragraph, the reader will not have any sense of priority. If something is 'even more important' then you need to discuss that topic earlier.

'Vital' is a vital word in the context of a lifesaving procedure or a correct prescription dose. But it is often used to describe things that are just mildly interesting to the author.

'Important' words

- crucial
- emphatic
- exciting
- imperative
- inescapable
- mandatory
- plethora
- significant (unless statistics)
- unique
- paramount

- dramatic
- essential
- fundamental
- important
- key
- markedly
- proliferation
- substantial
- vital

'Important' phrases

- do not underestimate how vitally important this is

- galvanised into action

- have a clear mandate to

- have an important role to play

- it cannot be emphasised strongly enough

- it is a requirement for everyone

- it is high time that nurses grasped the significance of...

- nothing short of a miracle

- nurses are in a unique position to...

- nurses would be well advised to...

- of paramount importance

- particular attention must be paid to

- the profession must acknowledge that...

- there is a very real need for...

- very important, very real

- vitally important

- we cannot escape the fact that

- we must recognise that

Sneaking in an opinion

In whose opinion is something important or essential? These words and phrases often blur the boundaries between objective writing (fact) and subjective writing (opinion). 'It is important that...' or 'It is essential that...' often allow writers to sneak their opinion into a piece of factual writing when they should say 'I believe that...' or 'In the author's opinion...' These imperatives can often be shortened to 'must' or 'should', for example:

it is essential that patients are...	patients should be...
it is essential that the change agent...	the change agent must
it is for this reason that it is essential	this is why you/they must

Prioritise

Sometimes 'important' words creep in later in a discussion. The writer has gathered more information and decided that this new information is more important than earlier material. Readers might already have given up because there is nothing to keep their interest. Don't be afraid to move copy around and put paragraphs in a different order.

Jim Robinson, Lecturer in Children's Nursing at Edinburgh University, says: 'You can make your point simply by paying attention to the structure of your prose. Don't lose important points in the later half of a paragraph when they should come earlier in the text. I also find it useful to summarise the main points in the introductory paragraph.'

Have a good read through. This helps you to re-structure and prioritise your work so that you do not have to tack important ideas on at the end.

Exercise: the chocolate test

Find a piece of work you have written. Save it with a different file name, for example choc.doc.

Use find and replace to find 'important' words from the list above.
Replace these 'important' words with the word 'chocolate'.

Now read your copy again. If you have overused the 'important' words you will soon feel queasy and uncomfortable.

Chapter 8

Ask yourself – is it that obvious?

"SO, WHERE ARE THE WOODS?"

8: Ask yourself – is it that obvious?

Writers often use phrases that assume the reader shares their opinion, or has followed their argument so far. If you use patronising language you can make your readers feel stupid and inferior, as if they haven't been paying attention.

Make sure your reader is with you
If you find yourself opening a paragraph with one of the words or phrases below, ask yourself – is everything as clear and as obvious to your reader as it is to you? Can you start your paragraph another way, for example with a new subheading?

'arguably' (sounds warning bells, the writer is going to state an opinion...)

'as has been established earlier in this article'

'as we have already seen'

'at the risk of sounding...' (negative way to open a sentence)

'clearly'

'for clarity, the tables show' (don't present tables if they are not clear)

'from the preceding information the reader should understand...'

'indubitably'

'inevitably'

'interestingly'

'in the view of the present author...' (author coming up with an opinion again. Can be shortened to 'I think that...')

'it can be seen that'

'it goes without saying that' (then why say it?)

'it is clear from this that'

'it is generally accepted that' (by whom?)

'it is important to realise that'

'it is interesting to note'

'it is not difficult to see from this that'

'it is not surprising, therefore, that...'

'many of you will have come across' (those who haven't will feel stupid)

'obviously'

'on the contrary' (is your first point clear enough to have a contrary?)

'one may well ask the question' (why didn't you ask it before?)

'quite frankly' (if this is so frank, there is no need to say it)

'tellingly'

'this begs the question'

'understandably'

'viewed in this light'

'we cannot escape the fact that...' (if this is so unavoidable, just go ahead and say it)

Appropriate, etcetera and so on

Peter Birchenall is Professor of Health Studies at the University of Lincolnshire and Humberside. His least favourite word is 'appropriate'. He says:

'This covers the author's inability to specify exactly what he or she means in certain situations. Phrases such as "an appropriate person" or "an appropriate place" are used instead of saying in plain words who the person is or identifying the place by name. Any interpretation is generally left to the reader. 'The word "inappropriate" is often used in an almost bullying way. It actually means, "don't argue – remember your place".'

Other phrases that assume your reader has followed the same lines of thought as you are 'etcetera' and 'so on and so forth'. How can your reader or listener possibly know what items you mean to add to your list? Either list more things, or stop at the last item you mentioned.

Chapter 9

Speak for yourself, not for your manager

'PATIENT-DRIVEN AMBULANCE SERVICE'

9: Speak for yourself, not for your manager

Many words and phrases seem to have crept into nursing from management consultants, politicians and public relations advisers. Jim Robinson, Lecturer in Children's Nursing at the University of Edinburgh, says: 'So many of these phrases seem to be deliberate attempts to hinder communication rather than foster it. Or they are simply irritating. I particularly dislike:

"I hear what you are saying" (I would prefer someone to listen to what I am saying)

"need-to-know basis" (so often used to mean everyone needs to know but I am only telling those I want to know about something)

"human resources" (whatever happened to people?)

Address this issue
'I address audiences and envelopes,' said one of the Plain Words workshop delegates, 'but I cannot bring myself to address issues'.

Neither can I, because I'm not sure whether it means:
- look at a problem (examine)
- solve a problem (deal with, tackle)
- look at and solve?

Another member of the team said of her head of department:

'It can sometimes be difficult to filter out what he is trying to say. His overuse of management-speak phrases during any conversation is so overwhelming that you forget what you asked him in the first place!'

Use sparingly
Like the 'important' words *(Keep it in perspective, Chapter 7)* the words opposite and overleaf can be used sparingly for seasoning and variety as long as their meaning is clear.

Phrase	Does it mean...?
against a backdrop of	while there is (for example) poverty/unemployment/violence
alligator wrestling versus draining the swamp	short-term remedies for long-term problems
at the end of the day	basically
back to basics	traditional ways
balance both ends against the middle	reach an agreement/consensus
belt and braces	don't miss anything out, or make sure
bottom line	what matters most
bottom up/top down	bottom up = action to reach goals top down = goals
breakout sessions	discussion groups; or (sometimes) coffee time
cascading information	letting staff know
core values	'the way we do things here'
downsizing	redundancies
forest fires	out of control, or problems without solutions
greyscale	uncertain
hit the ground running	get on without wasting time, or be prepared
I don't want the tiger by the tail to devour us	take care, this could be tricky
I have installed a new attitude	I would like you to try to work as a team
I hear what you're saying...	...usually followed by 'but', for example: I don't agree with you, or that idea won't work

Phrase	Does it mean...?
I would like to share with you...	let's talk about, or I haven't told you this yet, but...
internal briefing	letting staff know
it's a steep learning curve	I've had to learn a lot rather quickly, or I don't know what to do next or this isn't as easy as I thought
need-to-know basis	don't tell everyone
ongoing situation	still /no change
painted into a corner	we've run out of ideas/money/options
past its sell-by date	overdue, or an old idea
patient-driven	what you would do if you were the patient (patients are not usually able to drive anything. A patient-driven ambulance service would not be a great success!)
plug and play	we can use this idea straight away
proactive	anticipating, or thinking of it before someone else does
re-engineering	seeing if things can be done more effectively
reinvent the wheel	waste time doing something that's already been tried
run this one up the flagpole	try this idea out, or see how people react
seamless service	continuity, or good communication between departments
singing from the same hymnsheet	agreeing, or giving out the same message, or toeing the line, or speaking the same language

Phrase	Does it mean...?
spin doctor	public relations officer
stem the rising tide of	prevent or reduce
synergy	working together, sharing resources
tail wagging the dog	a small group is manipulating a larger group, or people are over-reacting to a small problem
touch base	let me know
touchy-feely	qualitative and hard to measure
very real danger	risk (something is either dangerous or it isn't)

Chapter 10

Cut the waffle

10: Cut the waffle

Christine Webb, Professor of Health Studies at the University of Plymouth, says: 'Saying things in a roundabout and supposed academic language just leads to long and rambling sentences.'

She recommends: 'Write as you speak, and never use a long word, phrase or sentence when you can find a shorter one – for example:

"the maintenance of" instead of "maintaining"
"the provision of" instead of "providing"
"within" instead of "in"
"upon" instead of "on"
"utilise" instead of "use".'

Woolly phrases
Here are some more examples of long-winded, woolly phrases (on the left) with suggested alternatives (on the right). Put a sheet of paper over the right-hand columns and work your way down the list.

For each pair, ask yourself:
- Do I already use the alternative?
- Is the alternative better?
- Is the alternative too simple for my style of writing?
Only you can decide how many of the suggestions you want to take up.

Phrase	Suggested alternatives
a couple of other points are worthy of mention here	just go ahead and mention them
a multifunctional, multidisciplinary proactive group of cohorts who enjoy networking over current research issues	research development team
absolutely	yes
act as troubleshooters for potential problems	look out for potential problems
acts to influence	influences

Phrase	Suggested alternatives
administer	give
by way of introduction	first,
cause to be...	make something...
commenced	started
concerning	about
despite the fact that a large proportion of	although many
exercise patience	be patient, wait and see
exercise restraint	restrain/hold back
experience difficulty with	find it hard to
given this, it would appear that	so
has a significance	is significant
has the appearance of	looks like/appears to be
have a clear understanding of	understand
have an effect on	affect
help to enable, help to assist	help
if at all possible	if possible/if you can
impacted on	affected
in a climate of (not meteorology)...	while there is poverty/inflation/violence/uncertainty
in a rapidly changing world	today, 1999, 2000...
in connection with	about
in need of	needs
in such a way as to render meaningless	this affects the results by...
in the absence of	without

Phrase	Suggested alternatives
is it any wonder, then, that...?	it is not surprising
it is our intention	we intend/we plan to
made privy to	was told/found out about
members of the local community	local people
non-application of funds	financial cuts
not uncommon	usual
on a weekly basis	weekly/every week
only served to exacerbate	made it worse
operate on the assumption	assume
paediatric cases	children
place emphasis upon	emphasise/stress
possess an awareness of	know about
predicated on a foundation	based on
provide with	give
relating to	about
retain mobility	stay mobile
revisit the debate	think again
served to increase staff morale	improved staff morale
serves to demonstrate	shows
serves to remind us	reminds us
similarities exist between A and B	A and B are similar
so badly needed	lacking
students receive little or no theoretical grounding	students are not taught very much about...
the incidence of suicide has increased	more people have killed themselves each year

Phrase	Suggested alternatives
the very fact that	that
the very idea	the idea
there may be detrimental consequences for the public	the public may suffer
they fall into a lower age group	they are younger
this gives a graphical representation of the paucity of advice given	this shows how little advice is given
this is the position in which we find ourselves	we are...
to all intents and purposes	basically (see Chapter 13)
underpinning philosophy	based on
very much so	yes
we made the necessary arrangements	we arranged
which brings us to the last question	finally,
will not necessarily be	may not be
without reference to the resource available to them	without working out if they could afford it
...whose presence may be essential in hospital	who may be needed in hospital

Exercises
Simplify these words and phrases (answers on page 79)

- a period of four hours
- apropos of
- believe there may be
- conceivably has
- enquires of
- give assistance

- in advance of the occasion
- in cases when
- in relation to
- not allow full development to
- not commonplace
- on the basis of
- on the matter/subject of
- optimal method
- recognised for what it is
- regarding
- require
- the extent to which
- the likelihood is
- there are instances when
- this procedure involves using
- will not necessarily be
- with respect/regard to

Try to get a copy of the Plain English Campaign's A-Z guide of alternative words (the address is on page 83). The words are in two columns – the 'hard' words on the left and the suggested alternatives on the right. As you have done in this chapter, cover up the right-hand column with a piece of paper. See how many of the hard words you can simplify. There are also good checklists in Gunning and Kallan (1994) pages 56-57 and 92-97.

Chapter 11

Ask a critical friend

11: Ask a critical friend

A friend who is critical? Surely not? Aren't friends there to flatter you and say 'mmm, that's great, that sounds just about right'? No. Real friends are honest and realistic. Critical friends are people who can read through your work before you print it. They can also listen to your presentation before you get up on the platform.

Sometimes people are afraid to ask their colleagues for advice. They send articles off to busy journal editors who may not have time to give constructive feedback with the rejection letter. They don't know if:
- their research is flawed
- their article is unsuitable for the journal's style and audience
- someone else has got there first with a similar subject, or
- if their writing has been so long-winded that the reviewers have given up on them.

If you have one article rejected, why bother working on another?

It's much better to fine-tune your work with people you know before you submit it to a journal. Your article is more likely to be accepted, and it may go through the publication process more quickly.

Jackie Solomon, Senior Nurse in Research and Development, Bolton Hospitals NHS Trust, says: 'Writing is a continuous learning experience. I have used the concept of a critical friend for a number of years now. Who that is very much depends on what I am writing. It has to be someone with whom I feel comfortable and who will provide constructive criticism.

'They should be linked with the readership for which my work is intended. In our trust we have established a list of proofreaders for patient information. These are volunteers from all areas, including Community Health Council members. If it's appropriate I may ask my family, and in some cases my elderly mother. I also have access to a PR officer in the trust who was a journalist. Writing workshops are useful, as are a number of my colleagues who have had papers published in journals.'

You
You can be your own best critical friend if you can put yourself in the position of reader or listener.

Read it out loud

Read your work out loud in front of the mirror. You may not notice on screen or paper if you have written in a stuffy, longwinded style. But it will soon come out when you read your words. If you find yourself reading a word or phrase in a silly voice or pulling a face, take note and try to rewrite the sentence. Don't write down anything you wouldn't feel comfortable saying out loud.

Take a break

Don't try to proofread your words the minute they roll off the printer, especially if you have been working long and hard at the screen. Take a break and come back to your work later. Number your pages, print out a draft (double-spaced) on rough paper and then leave it overnight – or longer if you can.

Focus

Clear your desk so that you only have the draft, a ruler, a pencil and a desk lamp in front of you. Put everything else in a cardboard box under the desk.

You are now editing your work, and you need a calm, uncluttered environment. If your desk is full of computer, sit somewhere else. You will not need to go back to the computer until you have finished reading your draft.

If you can, choose a time when your children, colleagues or the telephone will not interrupt you. Don't try to edit your work on a train or bus, or when you are hungry or tired.

With this fresh approach, you are more likely to:
- pick up spelling mistakes and typographical errors
- notice the mistakes that your spell checker doesn't pick up, such as 'from' for 'form' and 'you' for 'your'
- see where you have repeated yourself
- see where you have gone off the point
- see where you have missed out important information
- structure your work with headings and subheadings
- move copy around if you think it has a more logical order
- see where you have said something really silly

Your colleagues

Senior colleagues have broader experience and may understand your subject in greater depth. They can suggest which journals to approach and how to tailor your writing to those journals.

Your peers can support you. If they understand you and your work they will know how well your writing reflects the working practice in your department. You can bounce ideas off them, and they may think of things that you have missed out.

Junior colleagues may challenge some of your jargon or ideas that are difficult to grasp – but you need to assure them that you welcome their comments and questions and that no question is too stupid.

Experts

In your trust or college there are sure to be people – not necessarily nurses – who can help you with the finer points of your presentation. These may include:

- librarians
- statisticians
- audio-visual technicians
- graphic designers
- public relations officers
- web editors

Don't be afraid to ask for their help. Or to challenge them if they use a jargon of their own that you don't understand – a designer who talks about PMTs and bromides is not seeking a sedative for premenstrual tension but discussing stages in the printing process.

Your family and friends

If you cannot explain yourself to those closest to you, it will be hard to communicate with strangers. Read your work to members of your family and your friends. They will tell you – honestly – when you sound professional and authoritative and when you sound ridiculous.

Writing workshops

Simon Breed runs one-day writing workshops for nurses. He advises on all stages of publishing, from choosing journals, to presenting a manuscript for publication.

Writing Workshops can help you to:
- choose which journal to write for
- make the article fit the needs of the audience
- plan and structure an article
- present the manuscript in the best possible format for the editor

Simon believes that 'Writing is never easy – but we try to demonstrate that certain aspects can and should be exciting, even fun. The sessions are informal and non-threatening – we hope this approach removes many of the usual fears – of rejection when you don't get published and of criticism when you do.'

Editors

Editors are human, though Simon Breed thinks that 'many people fear the God-like creature who is to be at best revered and at worst downright feared. The editorial team is there to help people get published, not to wave a red pen around all day.'

An editor can be your critical friend, and publication can be a team effort between you both. But you can annoy editors if you waste their time and expect everything to be done for you. Even if your article needs some work to lick it into shape for publication, there are some things you can do to make things run smoothly:
- stick to the deadlines you are given
- follow the authors' guidelines for that journal
- keep within the recommended word length – don't send a whole dissertation and ask them if they are interested!
- follow the style for references – don't do Vancouver if their style is Harvard
- check that all the references are there
- minimise changes at proof stage
- keep all your disks virus-free
- be patient – don't keep ringing to find out when your article will be published

Chapter 12

Make sure your patients understand you

12: Make sure your patients understand you

'I am very glad to hear that you are preparing this book' says Christina Martin, PR Officer for Down Lisburn Health and Social Services Trust, 'because nurses unwittingly sometimes produce things that **terrify** patients. Just after I had joined the Trust, I was given a leaflet on leg ulcers to proofread. I couldn't understand part of it, and the part I could understand sounded horrific.'

Your patients will understand you better if:
- you don't use jargon
- you find out how much they already know
- you don't underestimate their pain or their anxiety
- you put yourself in their shoes
- you ask them if you have explained yourself clearly
- you encourage them to ask questions
- you don't patronise them

Jargon
'There are enough health care professionals who enjoy sounding important', says Phil Walmsley, Senior Nurse Manager for Children's Services at Nottingham City Hospital, 'without nurses adding to the numbers. I think nurses should see themselves as a translation service from medical to English language.'

In *Chapter 5, Challenge jargon*, I defined jargon as a word or phrase that you pass on without:
- understanding it yourself; and
- making sure that the next person – patient or professional – understands it in the same way

Phil had to console a very distraught elderly man who had been told he had coryza. 'When I explained that it meant the common cold' he says,' the man was ready to kill the consultant.'

Jargon isn't just a failure to explain technical terms. Even simple words or phrases can be misunderstood or misheard (see box opposite).

Take care to explain who's who in the care team. Doctor, Mr, Mrs, anaesthetist, registrar, house officer – they are all doctors, but the patient may not understand the difference. They can no longer make any assumptions about uniforms, white coats, or gender.

Don't let me be misunderstood
- A nurse tried to explain to a woman patient how to use suppositories. She wondered why the woman looked confused. The woman thought her 'back passage' was where she kept her bicycle, and that the suppositories needed to be put there to keep cool.
- A mother asked a nurse what two separate medicines were for. The nurse told her that one was for her child's chest, the other for her child's ear. The nurse left the mother to give the medicines – the mother poured the second medicine (an oral antibiotic) into the child's ear.
- A new mother was asked in a questionnaire if she thought that the discharge arrangements at the maternity hospital were satisfactory. She replied 'I thought the water in the bidets could be warmer'.
- Down Lisburn Trust now uses 'multiprofessional' rather than 'multidisciplinary; because patients confused 'discipline' with 'punishment'.
- 'Have you any aches?'
  'Course we got eggs, we breeds chickens!'

Find out how much they know
Phil Walmsley says: 'As a paediatric nurse I find communicating with patients relatively easy. This is because I have to ascertain what their level of understanding is before I talk to them. Before starting a conversation I make sure that we are communicating on the same level.'

If the patient uses terms they have picked up from TV, magazines, or the Internet, ask them to tell you what they think these terms mean. Make sure you both understand the terms in the same way.

Don't underestimate their pain
Many patients complain that health professionals trivialise their pain. You cannot describe someone else's pain as 'slightly', 'mild', 'a little bit' or 'fairly'. What they want to know is that you will do your very best to minimise the effects of treatment.

'You may experience mild discomfort.'

What does this mean? Patients need to know the nature of the discomfort – pain, nausea, vertigo – and how long they can expect it to last. For example:

'This might make you feel sick/dizzy/lightheaded for a few minutes/hours/days'

'A degree of swelling and fairly extensive bruising is normal'

Here, the patient wants to know:
- For how long will I be swollen and bruised?
- What can I put on the swellings and bruises to help them go down?
- What should I do if I am still worried about it after xx days?

Try: 'You may be swollen and bruised for a few days. You can ease this by…If this does not help come and see us again next …'

Don't underestimate their anxiety
'It's all over, nothing to worry about now' after an operation means that the anaesthetist can take a tea break. For the patient there is still plenty to worry about.

Gillian Fletcher, a trainer for the National Childbirth Trust and the College of Health, tells of a doctor who said this to a cancer patient:

'We did find a nasty little lump in there, but I can sort that out for you, so we'll have you in next week for a little op to remove it. There's nothing to worry about.'

Nothing to worry about? What about the anaesthetic? Post-operative infection? What exactly do you mean by 'nasty'? What happens if you don't get all the lump out? When can I go back to work? Who will look after the kids? How many of these 'little ops' have you done? Will I go to reception and find that you can't actually fit the 'little op' in for another six weeks?
You may be the nurse who has to answer all these tricky questions long after the consultant has gone home.

Don't patronise
It is hard to check a patient's understanding without being patronising, and easy to leave out important information.

'Have I explained it clearly?' is less patronising than 'Is that clear?'

'Is there anything else you would like to know?' is better than 'Any questions?'

Coulter et al (1998) recommend that language should:
- facilitate rather than prescribe
- promote participation
- avoid a 'doctor knows best' attitude

Have another look at the 'patronising' words and phrases in *Chapter 8: Is it that obvious?* and think about how you use them in speech. Never assume that anything is obvious to the patient.

Leaflets

Five minutes after a consultation, patients can only remember between 50-65% of what they have been told. (Silverman et al 1998, Gibbs et al 1990). What they do remember may not be enough for them to make a decision about their treatment.

Written information helps to back up the verbal message in four ways (Henderson et al 1999). Patients can:
- revisit the information at their own pace when they feel ready to do so
- check their understanding of the verbal message
- share and discuss information with relatives or carers
- ask for further advice if required

Diane Henderson and her colleagues at Wrexham Maelor Hospital Trust worked with their Patient Communication Group (PCG) to produce guidelines for good practice when providing written information about specific conditions. They faced a double challenge – to produce material in both plain English and plain Welsh. For ease of reading they recommend nine criteria (See overleaf).

Ease of reading
(Henderson et al 1999)

- write in direct language, addressing the reader as 'you' or 'your' and not 'the patient'
- ensure language that may cause offence has been avoided, for example 'a person who has epilepsy' not 'the epileptic'
- avoid the use of unnecessary abbreviations, for example SCBU instead of Special Care Baby Unit
- risks and areas of scientific uncertainty should be represented in numbers whenever possible, for example '18 out of 20'
- explain medical terminology and do not use medical jargon
- use everyday words and avoid unfamiliar ones
- ensure that sentences are on average not longer than 15-20 words in length
- use active verbs
- avoid unnecessary fillers

Put yourself in their shoes
You may have seen hundreds of patients with the same disease or condition. But if you have not had the condition yourself you may not be able to describe the symptoms, the treatment and the problems of daily living. Sometimes the patients are the experts. They are often happy to pass their knowledge and experience on to others.

A team from The King's Fund (Coulter et al 1998) collected 54 information materials – leaflets, videos and audiotapes – prepared for patients. They asked 62 patients and 28 clinical specialists to review these materials. They found that many of the materials:
- left out important information
- did not explain technical terms
- did not give a balanced view of the effectiveness of different treatment options
- ignored uncertainties
- did not encourage patients to take part in decision making

Coulter et al (1998) recommend that people who produce patient information 'use patients' questions as the starting point'. If you are thinking about producing patient information for the first time, I recommend The

King's Fund's POPPi Guide (Duman and Farrell 2000). POPPi stands for 'practicalities of producing patient information' and the guide leaves no stone of the process unturned. There is good advice on consulting patients with experience of a particular disease or condition.

For this type of work you should add patients to your list of critical friends *(see Chapter 11)*. If there is no patient group in your trust, invite patients who have attended your clinic in the past to suggest questions and look at early drafts of the leaflets you are preparing. Nationally there may be a charity or organisation that supports people with a particular condition. They may already have answered some of the questions that your patients ask. This can save you a lot of preliminary work.

Secker and Pollard (1995) offer useful advice for piloting (pre-testing) leaflets. In particular they advise you to encourage your patients to 'say what they really think'. They say: 'Patients are often so grateful for a service that they are unwilling to make any criticisms. When they do offer criticism, you need to be prepared to accept it and make any changes suggested.'

Be active and informal
In *Chapter 4: Be active,* I showed how passive verbs can clog up your academic writing and make it sound stuffy. They can also make you sound pompous in patient leaflets. For example:

Passive/formal	Active/friendly
Referrals are usually through your GP	Your doctor will usually arrange for you to see...
A full range of minor operations is undertaken in this practice	We do many minor operations here (even more helpful to list them)
Efforts are being made to reduce the delay	We will try not to keep you waiting
If you consider that your problems warrant an urgent consultation	If you need to see the doctor urgently
It is envisaged that...	We expect
You will be provided with assistance	We will help you
Medication may be indicated	Your doctor might prescribe tablets/medicine/suppositories ...

Passive/formal	Active/friendly
Patients are required to supply...	Please bring ...
This should not dissuade you	Do not be put off by
Transport can be arranged upon request	Let us know if you need an ambulance or taxi to bring you to the clinic or take you home
You will both be discharged on day three providing there are no complications	If everything is all right, you and your baby can go home on the third day
Return to work is dependent on your profession	Please tell your doctor or nurse if your work involves any of these activities: xx xx or xx
Further tests may be needed if clinically indicated	If this test shows that........., we might recommend that you take another test so that we can diagnose your condition more accurately, or If this treatment does not help, we might recommend that you take another test so that we can offer a different treatment
Care must be taken during bathing	Try to keep your dressing dry. If you do get it wet ...(give advice)
There is no need	You do not need

Centre for Health Information Quality (CHiQ)

The Centre for Health Information Quality (CHiQ) was launched in November 1997. It is a UK NHS initiative that aims to 'support the development of patient information that is:

- clearly communicated
- evidence-based
- involves patients'

CHiQ operates an enquiry service for anyone producing or disseminating consumer health information, although it cannot give patients information about specific conditions or diseases. CHiQ projects include PIPER, CHILI and QUIP.

PIPER
Patient Information Projects Exchange Register (PIPER) is a register of local and national initiatives in consumer health information. PIPER invites people developing patient information to share and benefit from the experiences of others.

CHILI
The Consumer Health Information Literature (CHILI) database provides details about:
- developing good quality evidence-based patient information
- evaluating existing materials
- explaining why these activities are important.

CHILI contains details of books, reports and journal articles

QUIP
The Quality Information for Patients (QUIP) database gives details of patient information materials tested for quality by CHiQ. So far, four topic areas have been covered. They are:
- back pain
- breast cancer
- cervical cancer
- rheumatoid arthritis

QUIP has tested printed materials for readability and the quality of their treatment option information. The database is expanding to test more topic areas and non-printed materials, including the Internet.

Plain English Campaign
The Plain English Campaign 'fights to promote the use of plain English and to stamp out all forms of gobbledygook – legalese, small print and bureaucratic language.'

The Campaign offers a number of professional services. These include:
- editing
- writing
- design
- training in plain English for trust employees

The Campaign gives annual awards for good use of plain English – and Golden Bull awards to organisations that are 'guilty of using impenetrable jargon'.

In 1990 the Plain English Campaign launched the Crystal Mark to encourage organisations to communicate clearly with the public. The Crystal Mark is a seal of approval for clearly written documents. Many NHS trusts have the Crystal Mark on their patient literature, and you will find some examples of good practice in the answers to the exercises for this chapter.

If your trust or college is hosting a Plain English training course try to book a place. You will learn a great deal about communicating at all levels.

The Campaign has published several books. They include *Utter Drivel,* which contains one of the best and most amusing examples of National Health 'impenetrable jargon' (see opposite). You'll find a list of other books and the Campaign's address on pages 82-83.

Christina Martin, Public Relations Officer for Down Lisburn Health and Social Services Trust, consulted the Plain English Campaign when she prepared patient information for her trust. She says: 'The most important thing I learnt was to think hard about the intended audience for the information and to put myself as far as possible into their shoes. They offered some simple pointers on style that I found useful:
- not using capitals for headings
- using bold for emphasis
- bullet points
- use of active voice
- use of 'we' and 'you'
- shorter sentences
- less jargon

Exercises
The answers to these exercises (on page 80) are extracted from some patient information leaflets that have been awarded the Plain English Campaign's Crystal Mark.
- define counselling and list four ways that counselling can help
- what is a prosthesis?
- what is a prosthetist?
- an outpatient may need to see the doctor again. Explain what they should do
- describe a stoma
- define self-medication and how it works in your department

What is a Bed?
(Plain English Campaign, 1994)
A device or arrangement that may be used to permit a patient to lie down when the need to do so is a consequence of the patient's condition rather than a need for active intervention such as examination, diagnostic investigation, manipulative treatment, obstetric delivery or transport.

Beds, couches, or trolleys are also counted as hospital beds where:

a) Used regularly to permit a patient to lie down rather than for merely examination or transport. (E.g. in a day surgery ward.)
b) Used whilst attending for a specific short procedure taking an hour or less, such as endoscopy, provided that such devices are used only because of the active intervention and not because of the patient's condition.
c) Used regularly as a means of support for patients needing a lengthy procedure such as renal dialysis (includes special chairs etc.)
d) Used regularly to allow patients to lie down after sedation.
N.B. A device specifically and solely for the purpose of delivery should not be counted as a bed.

Available staffed beds: occupied or ready for occupation on the last day of the quarter under review, i.e. in which patients are being or could be treated without any changes in facilities or staff being made.

Includes cots in special care baby units and intensive therapy units for babies. Excludes:
a) Labour (first and second stage) as distinct from maternity beds.
b) Beds in reception wards, unless in permanent use in psychiatric hospitals.
c) Temporary beds (or stretchers) unless in permanent use in psychiatric hospitals.
Temporary bed: erected additional to the ward complement and dismantled within 24 hours of being erected. A bed erected for an emergency, but left up on account of pressure for a succession of patients, should be regarded as a temporary bed until dismantled.
d) Observation or recovery beds used for only a few hours, whether in out-patients departments or recovery units.

Chapter 13

Speak plainly

13: Speak plainly

Lord Greville Janner, QC wrote to 'The Times' suggesting a campaign to ban the words 'basically' 'actually' and 'essentially' from everyday speech. He said:

'Basically, if we could remove those words, it would actually add to the time that is essentially available for meaningful language by anything up to a third. And you would remove what is actually, basically and essentially an irritating substitute for "um" which at least has the virtue of brevity.'

Some people have irritating habits when they speak that should never be committed to paper. 'Basically', 'essentially',' actually' and 'um' are just a few of them. I asked the 'Plain Words' team to tell me what was most likely to send them off to sleep – or shopping – in a lecture or conference presentation.

Some factors are outside the speaker's control – you can't help it if someone in the audience has a heavy lunch or a hangover. Even the most thrilling of presentations won't keep them awake. Some people (I'm one of them) just drop off to sleep as soon as the lights go down. Poor acoustics and whistling microphones aren't your fault either, but if you allow some rehearsal time before your presentation you may be able to put things right.

Presentation problems
Your audience won't be impressed by:
- acetates of tables that are unreadable from the front, let alone the back
- hi-tec slides that look gorgeous and say absolutely nothing
- slides that are out of order
- slides or acetates for which there is no projector
- tables of figures that don't add up
- dark and boring slides
- slides with too much information on
- writing that is too small to read from the front, let alone the back
- graphs that don't give any information
- (you can't win!) no visual aids at all
- too many facts and figures
- old information

Speaker sins
Never:

- apologise for your work
- run over your allotted time
- read from your acetates or slides without looking up
- read in a monotonous voice
- jangle keys in your pockets
- walk around
- leave no time for questions
- tap the microphone
- whistle or waffle inanely if the microphone or projectors go wrong and your presentation is delayed
- gallop through your presentation without giving the audience the chance to write things down
- go into unnecessary detail
- go off at a tangent

Wrong words
Don't say:

- you won't be able to read this
- sorry, this doesn't appear to be working
- er, that's it
- I'll answer that later
- i.e.
- e.g.
- um
- er
- sort of
- kinda
- you know
- d'you see
- etcetera
- and so on ...and so forth

Golden oldies
When you speak, do you still utter such golden oldies as:

- notwithstanding
- furthermore
- aforesaid
- whereas
- whatsoever
- hereinafter
- heretofore?

If you do, watch out for people yawning and falling off their chairs. These words are part of the rich heritage of the English language – but they are also very old-fashioned.

Your audience will be happy if you...
- check that the presentation equipment is working before the session begins – it does not create a good impression to see a presenter fumbling with equipment or not knowing where the on/off switch is
- involve them and ask them questions
- apply your presentation to their experience and area of practice – make them feel as if it has been tailor-made for them
- involve them
- are up to date with current thinking
- make them laugh with anecdotes and humorous stories
- change the pace and technique of your presentation every 20 minutes or so
- look at them
- give your presentation a clear structure – tell them what you're going to cover, keep to the point and summarise your main points at the end
- use one acetate or slide about every 3-5 minutes
- stick to the point
- practise your presentation so that the key words on the acetate prompt you and create a flow
- can sense when they are losing interest and do something about it
- are enthusiastic about your subject

Chapter 14

Make sure your numbers are clear

14: Make sure your numbers are clear

However plain your words, you can still wreck your work by including numbers that don't make sense. Ask yourself these questions:
- are my numbers reader-friendly?
- do I know what I am talking about?
- how good are my numbers?
- is my work limited?
- does this table, graph or chart enhance what I have already written, or is it confusing?
- who can help?

Are my numbers reader-friendly?
Think about your numbers from your readers' point of view:
- if you start a sentence – as many do – with 'As Figure 1 clearly shows…' can you honestly say that Figure 1 will be as clear to your readers as it is to you?
- if you give too much information they may lose touch with the subject you are discussing. Select the data that best illustrate your main points
- if you give too little information, they may wonder why you bothered to mention the figures at all
- if your numbers or percentages don't add up – and you don't explain why – your readers may start to doubt your words
- they will also start to doubt your words if you use statistical tests or charts that aren't appropriate for your data

Do I know what I am talking about?
In *Chapter 5: Challenge jargon,* I said that any word could be jargon if you do not explain your understanding of that word to another person. This often happens when designing a research study. You may think you understand, for example, 'false longitudinal design' or 'triangulation'. Your readers' understanding of these terms, if they have one, may not be the same as yours. They may read your work in a way you never intended.

How good are my numbers?
'Robust' has become a key word for data and the tools we use to handle data. Though a 'robust instrument' – jargon in itself – may remind you of a tuba, it is a good way to describe the comprehensive software, such as the Statistical

Package for the Social Sciences (SPSS) now available to analyse and present your results. Before you pour your data into one of these computer packages, remember:

- your data must be right for the software
- the software must be right for your data

Tables, graphs and charts

Calling something a graphical representation (or graphical illustration) is pompous and windy. Many things have been described as graphical representations:

- tables
- graphs
- flow charts
- gory photographs
- pie charts
- bar charts
- line drawings

Say what you mean.

Here are some appropriate uses for different types of chart.

Type of chart	Best used to show
Bar	numbers of items in each category
Line	trends
Area	trends
Pie	numbers of items in each categories (beware: too many categories mean too many slices)
Scatter	relationships between variables
Boxplot	differences between groups
Histogram	the shape of a distribution

Is my work limited?

Sometimes researchers present sample sizes of very small numbers – usually just of immediate peers or students – as definitive. Is your study limited in size or scope? If so, it may be better to spell out your limitations than to go to two decimal places of probability to prove yourself. You may identify weaknesses in your work, but your readers will respect your honesty in admitting them. Instead of getting bogged down in figures, they will assess more quickly:

- how your work could be developed with larger or different groups
- where you went up blind alleys that are not worth pursuing

When you are discussing limitations, think about your readers. If they are other researchers, you may need to discuss the technical aspects of your analysis. If they are practitioners, you may need to discuss whether the limitations of your research mean that it cannot yet be used in practice.

Confounding variables

When you compare, say, patients' responses to different treatments, you want the groups you are comparing to be well matched for other factors such as age, sex and social class. If your groups are not well matched, you won't be able to tell if your results are due to the different treatments or to these other 'confounding' variables.

Use the phrase 'confounding variables' with care, and not as an apology for unexplained hiccups in your data. All variables can confound your reader if you don't explain them clearly.

- if what you really mean is *'I don't really understand what happened here'* or *'I couldn't control for variable X'* then be honest enough to say so. You may save someone else from going up a dead end with their own investigation
- list your confounding variables and explain fully why you are concerned about them; or
- forget the confounding variables and home in on those figures that do stand up to scrutiny and support your work

Subdivided percentages

Subdivided percentages are hard to interpret. For example:
'93 per cent returned the questionnaire, of which 56 per cent were grade F. Of these, 43 per cent were female.'

Does the writer mean 56 per cent of 93 per cent or of the total sample size? Do they mean 43 per cent of 56 per cent, of 93 per cent or the total sample size? Is the number of women in Grade F more important than the total number of women who responded?

Who can help?

In *Chapter 11 – Critical friends* – we show you how other people can help you present your words clearly. Don't be afraid to seek advice on your numbers from statisticians and researchers who have experience with the data you are presenting.

Chapter 15
Be clear online

15: Be clear online

Everything I have said about presenting plain words on paper applies to pages on the World Wide Web (WWW). Unfortunately, many people still post up page after page of poorly-written text without using the many new facilities that the Web offers. Bad writing is just as difficult to read on screen as it is on paper.

What's good about the WWW?

You learn to organise your ideas
All written work – on screen or on the printed page – needs a structure. As we use the WWW more we may start to think and write more logically. Instead of starting at the beginning and rambling on to fill a quota of words, we will map out our work more carefully.

We will work on smaller chunks of text – people browsing the Web find it easier to move to another page that interests them than to scroll down the same page.

As we go, we will use headings and sub-headings and identify how the parts of our work link with each other and with other work. We will learn how to do this with hypertext – the programming that links pages and ideas. Hypertext may be closer to the way we think than starting at A and going through to Z.

You can share your ideas immediately
You can change the content of Web pages daily or even hourly. 'This changes our concepts of drafts and final versions,' says Rod Ward, Lecturer in Nursing at the University of Sheffield. 'With the ability to communicate rapidly we will develop new ways to share ideas and collaborate with people in other countries and other disciplines.'

And because the Web is worldwide, words you post at teatime will arrive in the USA in time for lunch, and in Australia in time for tomorrow's breakfast.

You can illustrate your work better
The Web offers many new ways to present our work. Multimedia – graphics, photographs, animations, film and sound clips – can all help us to illustrate our words in a way that paper publishing can not. At the moment many people are frustrated by the speed of downloading these elements. This will

improve as modems get faster and the new broadband technology – which sends more signals through a single wire – becomes more widely available.

What's bad about the WWW?

What you see may not be what they get
There is one big difference between journal publishing and publishing on the WWW. Every subscriber to a paper journal will see the same colours, layout and typefaces on the page. But however lovely your web site looks on your screen, your reader may see something different. They may have a different 'browser' – software for accessing information on the web. Microsoft Internet Explorer and Netscape Navigator are the most commonly used browsers and can show most of the graphics. But some people may only be able to read text. And if their modem is slow, they may choose to turn off the graphics.

You can overcome the problem by sending your document to the Web in a portable document format (.pdf). This doesn't change the layout of your original and keeps all its design features. To read this, the person at the other end will need to download a simple package (usually Adobe Acrobat Reader). This is a good way of sending long reports or documents with lots of diagrams.

You might lose your reader
There is plenty of scope for distraction on the Web. If your illustrations take up too much file space they will take ages to appear on screen and a reader with a slow modem may give up, preferring to watch paint dry or grass grow. One person might enter the literature review and then link up with other writers on the same subject; another may go straight to your results or the implications for practice without reading the background material. Skipping from abstract to findings is common. Or they may go off to a completely different site.

Always make sure that your reader:
- can get back to your home page
- can easily find your e-mail address and your phone and fax numbers and postal address if you want to use them

People will lose the skill to write originally
Already we can download and copy material from a number of sources, whether or not we are allowed to do so. It will be very easy to plagiarise and

breach other people's copyright – and for them to breach yours. We may put together a dreadful patchwork of styles and lose the skill to write originally. Teachers are already identifying this problem with their pupils' homework.

No substitute for books

Ciolek (1996) expressed the fear that the WWW would become MMM ('Multi-Media Mediocrity'). Phil Walmsley, Senior Nurse Manager for Children's Services at Nottingham City Hospital, says: 'The fact that the text is printed gives it an authority that mere spoken words do not have. I am aware how quickly the rubbish that I am spouting takes on an authoritative air as it becomes printed text.'

Phil believes that we will eventually need to go back to reading, 'simply to ensure that what you are looking at has had some external scrutiny.'

'If external scrutiny is to be applied to the Internet then it will cost, and as such there becomes little difference between reading the book on the net and buying it (which is now remarkably easy due to the Internet) in real terms. I do not think that you will ever get to a stage where we read directly from the net – the feel of a book will remain important.'

How to publish on the WWW

Find your way around

Get used to using the Web – look at lots of different sites on professional and leisure subjects that interest you. You can 'save' web site addresses you want to visit again using 'bookmark' (Netscape Navigator) or 'favorites' (Microsoft Internet Explorer). Make a note of sites and presentations you like (and dislike).

Get help

Designing a website from scratch isn't difficult, but it is time-consuming, and you are a busy health professional already! Don't battle ahead on your own if there is someone in your trust or college who is employed to put web pages together and understands how to lay out and link your copy.

A teenager may be keen to help for a school Information Technology project – but take care that they don't put so much groovy stuff on it that they lose your message.

There are heaps of books and websites to help you. Some are more technical than others. My favourite for plain words and clear graphics is Ruth Maran's Creating Web Pages Simplified (Maran Graphics 1999).

Web editors

A lot of computer coding – called hypertext mark-up language (HTML) – goes into even the simplest of websites. All the coding must be exact – one misplaced / or > or " may mean a missing link or a wrong format. When you learn to drive you don't need to understand everything that happens under the bonnet of your car, and you don't need to learn HTML to design a website.

A good way to start is to use 'what-you-see-is-what-you-get' (WYSIWYG) editing software such as Netscape Composer, Adobe Page Mill or Microsoft Front Page, or others you can download free from the Web. You set out your document as you would in your word processor – using bold, italics, tables, colours and headline styles till it looks the way you want it. You can edit and spell check in this view. All the coding is done for you. To make a link you highlight text or graphics, click 'link' and paste in the address of the page or site you want to link to.

Work out how people will navigate round your site

Think how you will guide your reader round your site. Put the reader in control by providing a range of menu bars or options. See how other sites do this. Always think about where your reader might want to go next.

Break up your text

Web readers do not want to scroll down through pages of tiny text, especially if they are still online and paying for the phone. Use your links to encourage them to move between pages.

Lay out your page for horizontal viewing and invite your readers to set up their printer for 'landscape' (horizontal) rather than 'portrait' (vertical) printing. Then try to keep the main body of your text to no more than 200 words in three or four 50-word paragraphs. Give each page a unique subject heading.

You may find this 'chunky' approach hard to begin with, but it will help you to focus on the words that matter.

Arrange your topics

Write all your subject headings on a separate piece of scrap paper (or use old business cards) and arrange them on a table. Think about the order and priority of your topics and how you want to link them to your home page. Draw a tree that shows these links.

Pilot

When you have poured your words into your site and made all the links you want, ask someone else to have a look *(see Critical friends, Chapter 11).* Ask them:

- is it easy to read?
- is it well organised?
- does it look good?
  - not too plain
  - not too fussy
- do the links work?

Incorporate their comments. If you can, look at your site in other browsers.

Go online

When you are happy with your site – and not before – you are ready to show it to the world. Maran (1999) shows you in general terms how to upload your site (put it on the web) and sometimes you can get good advice from your internet service provider (the company you use to connect to the internet). Go to their website or phone their technical desk for a step-by-step guide.

Once you have uploaded your site you will need to visit it to double-check that everything is working as it should and that the download times are not too slow.

Spread the (key) word

People need to find your site, and they are likely to do this using key words in a search engine such as Yahoo! or Google. For example, to promote this book I might choose:

PLAIN, WORDS, CLEAR, ENGLISH, WRITE, WRITING, NURSE, NURSES, MIDWIFE, MIDWIVES and put them at the top of the coding in my document. This increases the chance of someone finding my site with one or more of these keywords.

Answers to exercises

3: Answer the question
(page 12)
1 usually
2 mainly because
3 two weeks
4 most

4: Be active
(page 18)
1 GPs have been reluctant to…
2 Patients complete these surveys
3 We recommend that… or
   They recommend that…

6: Say it only once
(page 25)
developing ~~further~~
~~in circumstances~~ where
my ~~own~~
still ~~ongoing~~
then ~~subsequently~~
~~yet~~ another
consensus of ~~opinion~~

10: Cut the waffle
(page 45)

a period of four hours	four hours
apropos of	about
believe there may be	think, suspect
conceivably has	may have
enquires of	asks
give assistance	help
in advance of the occasion	before……happens
in cases when	when
in relation to	about
not allow full development to	limit
not commonplace	unusual
on the basis of	based on

on the matter/subject of	about
optimal method	best way
recognised for what it is	recognised
regarding	about
require	need
the extent to which	how far
the likelihood is	probably
there are instances when	sometimes
this procedure involves using	this procedure uses
will not necessarily be	may not
with respect/regard to	about

12: Make sure your patients understand you
(page 62)

1 Counselling is a way of helping you to:
• understand more about yourself and your problems
• deal with loss or anger
• tackle specific problems
• examine your feelings and look at things in a different way
(Southern Birmingham Community Health NHS Trust)

2 A prosthesis is a replacement for part of your body, for example an artificial leg or arm, an artificial eye, or an artificial heart valve.

3 A prosthetist is a person who is specialised in fitting and caring for someone who needs a prosthesis. *(Southern Birmingham Community Health NHS Trust)*

4 After the doctor has seen you, they may ask you to make another appointment. Please make this with the receptionist before you leave the department. If you are not sure when the doctor wants to see you again, please check with the clinic nurse or receptionist. *(Hairmyres and Stonehouse Hospitals NHS Trust)*

5 A stoma is an opening that is made through the right or left side of your abdomen, depending on whether you are having a colostomy, ileostomy or a urostomy. A bag is worn over this 'stoma' to collect waste from your body. *(Glasgow Royal Infirmary NHS Trust)*

6 Some patients like to be responsible for keeping and taking their own medicines, tablets and inhalers while in hospital. Other patients prefer the nurses to give them their medicines. Please discuss which you would prefer with a nurse. *(York District Hospital)*

References

Breed S (1999) A Publication Guide to 40 Health Care Journals. London, SB Communications. ISBN: 0953592502

Ciolek T (1996) Today's WWW – Tomorrow's MMM? The Specter of Multi-Media Mediocrity. Computer 29, 106-108

Coulter A, Entwhistle V, Gilbert D (1998) Informing Patients. An assessment of the quality of patient information materials. London, King's Fund. ISBN: 1857172140

Duman M, Farrell C (2000) The POPPi Guide: practicalities of producing patient information. London, King's Fund. ISBN: 1857174097

Foundation of Nursing Studies (1997) Reflection for Action. London, FoNS

Gibbs S, Waters W, George C (1990) Communicating information to patients about medicine. Journal of the Royal Society of Medicine. 83:292-297

Gunning R, Kallan R (1994) How to take the fog out of business writing Fourth Edition. Chicago, Dartnell

Hamill C (1999) Academic essay writing in the first person: a guide for undergraduates. Nursing Standard. 13, 44: 38-40

Henderson D, Jones J, Lord, S (1999) Don't Let the Ink Dry. Guidelines for the production of good quality condition-specific patient information and how to share information with other Welsh Trusts

Plain English Campaign (1994) Utter Drivel: a decade of jargon and gobbledygook. London, Robson Books. ISBN: 086051949X

Plain English Campaign. A-Z of alternative words. New Mills, Plain English Campaign. (available free at www.plainenglish.co.uk/A-Z.html)

Secker J, Pollard R (1995) Writing Leaflets for Patients. Edinburgh, Health Education Board for Scotland. ISBN: 1873452713

Silverman J (1998) Skills for communicating with patients. Oxford, Radcliffe Medical Press. ISBN: 1857751892

Further reading

Plain words
Bryson B (1997) Troublesome Words. Harmondsworth, Penguin. ISBN: 0140266402

Burnard P (1996) Writing for Health Professionals (second edition). London, Chapman & Hall. ISBN: 0412719800

Hartwell Fiske R (2000) Thesaurus of Alternatives to Worn-Out Words and Phrases. Lincoln, Nebraska, Universe.Com. ISBN: 0595000053

Hartwell Fiske R (1997) The Writer's Digest Dictionary of Concise Writing. Cincinnati, Ohio, Writer's Digest Books. ISBN: 0898797551

Young P (1996) The Art and Science of Writing. London, Chapman & Hall. ISBN: 0412599104

Plain numbers
Anthony D (1996) A review of statistical methods in the Journal of Advanced Nursing. Journal of Advanced Nursing 24, 1089-1094

Anthony D, Hicks C (1999) Understanding Advanced Statistics. Edinburgh, Churchill Livingstone. ISBN: 0443059330

Bryman A, Cramer D (1999) Quantitative Data Analysis with SPSS Release 8 for Windows. London, Routledge. ISBN: 0415206979

World Wide Web
Maran R (1999) Creating Web Pages with HTML Simplified (second edition) New York, Hungry Minds ISBN: 076460670

Addresses

Foundation of Nursing Studies
32 Buckingham Palace Road, London SW1W 0RE
Tel 020 7233 5750
Fax 020 7233 5759
Email admin@fons.org
www.fons.org

Writing Workshops
15 Mandeville Courtyard, 142 Battersea Park Road
London SW11 4NB
Tel 020 7627 1510
Fax 020 7627 1570
Email:simon@sbcommunicationsgroup.com
www.sbcomm.dial.pipex.com/wwabout.html

Plain English Campaign
PO Box 3, New Mills, High Peak, SK22 4QP
Tel 01663 744409
Fax 01663 747038
Email info@plainenglish.co.uk
www.plainenglish.co.uk

Centre for Health Information Quality
Highcroft, Romsey Road, Winchester, Hampshire SO22 5DH
Tel 01962 849100
Fax 01962 949079
Email admin@hfht.org
www.hfht.org/chiq/

DISCERN
If you are writing patient information about treatment choices, you may find the questionnaire on the DISCERN website a helpful guide to the standards of information that patients expect.
www.discern.org.uk/

Feedback

We would really like to hear your comments about this book.

Please give feedback via the Plain Words web page:

www.fons.org/projects/plainwds.htm

or email theresa.shaw@fons.org

or Fax to: 020 7232 5759

Have you enjoyed reading *Plain Words for Nurses?*

Do you think the book will help you to write/speak more clearly?

Which section was particularly helpful?

Are there other words and phrases that you particularly dislike and didn't see here?

Were there any sections where you disagreed with the content?

If the book is published again, what changes would you like to see?

Would you like to join an online newsgroup to discuss the way that health professionals communicate?

Name..

Contact address ....

....

Telephone no ....

Email ....

Institution.. Position ....

Thank you

Alison Turnbull